THIS JOURNAL BELONGS TO

_____

_____

_____

MY BADASS JOURNAL

ISBN-13: 978-0-578-93867-7

Regan Press

MY BADASS JOURNAL

A self-love journal to free
your Badass, get you empowered,
and help you actually live
a blissful life.

SHEILA KAMUDA

R

Regan Press

MY BADASS JOURNAL

A SELF-LOVE JOURNAL TO FREE YOUR BADASS, GET YOU EMPOWERED, AND ACTUALLY HELP YOU LIVE A BLISSFUL LIFE.

Packed with 52 powerful prompts, one for every week of the year, inspirational quotes and a Badass manifesto, broken down into 10 bite-size principles, this guided journal will lead you on a journey to uncover your power, make no apologies for your you-ness, and give you the confidence to own it, be it, do it.

About the Author

Sheila Kamuda is a success coach, speaker and writer, and the inspiration behind Live Out Loud Coaching. Prior to coaching, she spent 15 years leading teams to phenomenal success. Her passion is uplifting, shifting, and helping people live a blissful life. Having grown up in New York, and spending some magnificent years in her beloved Chicago, she is a city girl through and through.

Sheila created *My Badass Journal* for anyone on this planet who wants to go for their dreams. She believes there is nothing better than knowing you have power, accessing it, and loving yourself in the process.

Sheila Kamuda
liveoutloudcoaching.com

For Sydney,

whose inner light
always helps me find my way.

PROLOGUE

Whether you are loving your career, in between jobs, or a person living on this planet, you'll find in these pages insights, inspirations, and writing activities that will help you focus on the things you really want, live a life of empowerment, and be the Badass you are meant to be.

The path that led me to write this journal was a desire to help others realize that without empowerment, all the career strategies in the world will only go so far. Without empowerment, you continue to doubt yourself and your abilities. Without empowerment, you feel stuck, and cannot find real joy in your personal or professional life.

I came to understand empowerment through my own personal struggles after my husband passed away. It was a long journey, and I learned there is nothing better than knowing you have power, accessing it, and loving yourself in the process.

Shifting perspective can be light, and fun, and bold. Have fun with the journal. Enjoy embodying the Badass you are.

BADASS MANIFESTO

NO APOLOGIES

YOU HAVE POWER

SAY YES TO YOUR PAST

SPEAK YOUR TRUTH

NO CONVINCING

HIT THE "SEND" BUTTON

YOU GET TO CHOOSE

YOU ARE EXACTLY WHERE YOU SHOULD BE

LISTEN TO YOUR INNER VOICE; NOT YOUR INNER CRITIC.

ENOUGH

I'M GOING TO MAKE
EVERYTHING AROUND ME
BEAUTIFUL — THAT WILL
BE MY LIFE.

- Elsie de Wolfe-

Badass Manifesto #1

No Apologies

Do you like quiet time? How about dressing up for the Oscars? Do you love crossword puzzles? Dancing while you dust? Red wine or white?

Are you good at writing poetry? Building furniture? Problem solving? Fixing cars? Cooking meals from scratch? Having patience?

Whatever you like or dislike, are good at or not so much, you do you. Make no apologies for your you-ness.

PROMPT #1

I would do this every day if
I could...

_____

_____

_____

_____

_____

_____

_____

_____

_____

_____

_____

_____

PROMPT #2

I give myself permission to...

_____

_____

_____

_____

_____

_____

_____

_____

_____

_____

_____

_____

PROMPT #3

I don't "need" anyone to be
proud of me. I'm proud of me
for the time I...

PROMPT #4

Nothing makes me laugh
as much as...

_____

_____

_____

_____

_____

_____

_____

_____

_____

_____

_____

_____

PROMPT #5

Today I will not be afraid of...

_____

_____

_____

_____

_____

_____

_____

_____

_____

_____

_____

IF YOU CAN'T LOVE YOURSELF,
HOW IN THE HELL YOU GONNA
LOVE SOMEBODY ELSE?

- Ru Paul-

Badass Manifesto #2

You Have Power

You think you're powerless? You have the power to change things. Starting small is okay.

Think Ruby Slippers. Dorothy had the power all along. She just didn't realize how to access it.

There is also power in the words you speak, so no negative self talk. Ever.

You have power. Believe it. Know it. Own it.

PROMPT #6

My friends describe me like this...

PROMPT #7

I love conversations about...

_____

_____

_____

_____

_____

_____

_____

_____

_____

_____

_____

_____

_____

PROMPT #8

When I need comfort, I...

_____

_____

_____

_____

_____

_____

_____

_____

_____

_____

_____

_____

_____

PROMPT #9

These are my successes, big
& little...

_____

_____

_____

_____

_____

_____

_____

_____

_____

_____

_____

_____

_____

PROMPT #10

I am going to write down
all the stuff that makes
me feel good...

_____

_____

_____

_____

_____

_____

_____

_____

_____

_____

_____

_____

BE YOURSELF.
EVERYONE ELSE
IS ALREADY TAKEN.

- Oscar Wilde -

Badass Manifesto #3

Say Yes to Your Past

Accept everything. The good, the bad, and the ugly. That horrible stuff you went through is why you are so magnificent now. Simply put, you need all of you. Every bit.

So just accept it and dare I say, stop trying to figure out why. Just know that this is part of you. When you see this, you will come into your full self, your full brilliance. Your full magnificence.

Say Yes.

PROMPT #11

When the shit hits the fan,
I know it's time for me to grow
(again). This is one of those
times...

PROMPT #12

I am writing a "love letter"
to myself...

Dear _____

_____

_____

_____

_____

_____

_____

_____

_____

_____

_____

_____

_____

PROMPT #13

I don't have to convince anyone
of anything. I can just be me.
Here's one way I am truly me.

PROMPT #14

It's ok if I'm not perfect and some things are not in my wheelhouse. Here's what I'd rather not do...

PROMPT #15

This is the stuff I am really,
really, really good at...

_____

_____

_____

_____

_____

_____

_____

_____

_____

_____

_____

_____

_____

I AM THE MASTER
OF MY FATE.

I AM THE CAPTAIN
OF MY SOUL.

- William Ernest Henley -

Badass Manifesto #4

Speak Your Truth

Don't be afraid to show the world who you are.

You have a voice. Trust what you believe in, and make sure you're being true to your story, and not someone else's story.

Don't follow the others if it isn't your truth. If you don't align, that's okay.

Always speak your truth.

PROMPT #16

Sometimes I dream about...

PROMPT #17

I absolutely LOVE this
about myself...

PROMPT #18

I'm going to stop "shoulding" on myself. Here's my list of "shoulds" I am ditching...

PROMPT #19

Finish the sentence
"I Am _____"
with one of the words below.

Authentic
Brilliant
Creative
Curious
Daring
Determined
Enthusiastic
Funny
Grateful
Happy
Hopeful
Radiant
Relaxed
Sassy
Unapologetic
Unique

PROMPT #20

I feel so good I had the
gumption to go after this!

_____

_____

_____

_____

_____

_____

_____

_____

_____

_____

_____

_____

_____

DON'T LOOK AT YOUR FEET TO SEE IF YOU ARE DOING IT RIGHT.

JUST DANCE.

-Anne Lamott-

Badass Manifesto #5

No Convincing

You do not have to hard sell anyone. Not your boss, or potential employer, friends, your partner, or family. No one.

You don't have to convince anyone to follow you or understand you. You just need to be you. And if there's a match, that's great. If not, it's great too.

No convincing. Ever.

PROMPT #21

I love that I get to choose the
mood I want. Today, I choose...

_____

_____

_____

_____

_____

_____

_____

_____

_____

_____

_____

_____

_____

PROMPT #22

One day I'm going to learn
how to...

PROMPT #23

If I could meet anyone, it
would be...

_____

_____

_____

_____

_____

_____

_____

_____

_____

_____

_____

_____

_____

_____

PROMPT #24

Everything happens as it's
supposed to. I believe this
because...

_____

_____

_____

_____

_____

_____

_____

_____

_____

_____

_____

_____

_____

_____

_____

PROMPT #25

When I was a kid, I used to...

_____

_____

_____

_____

_____

_____

_____

_____

_____

_____

_____

_____

_____

_____

_____

CAN YOU REMEMBER
WHO YOU WERE, BEFORE THE
WORLD TOLD YOU WHO
YOU SHOULD BE?

-Danielle LaPorte-

Badass Manifesto #6

Hit the "Send" Button

You have an idea. Or a solution to a problem. Or a poem, or music, or illustration you've been working on.

You have two choices:
1. Keep it to yourself for fear the world won't like it, will laugh at you, or ignore you.

2. Be brave. Know that it is brilliant. Start caring about what *you* think more than what anyone else thinks. Do it for you.

Hit the "Send" Button.

PROMPT #26

What people don't know
about me is...

_____

_____

_____

_____

_____

_____

_____

_____

_____

_____

_____

_____

_____

_____

_____

_____

PROMPT #27

When I need to escape,
this is where I go...

PROMPT #28

My favorite movie is...

And this is why...

PROMPT #29

Home to me is...

_____
_____
_____
_____
_____
_____
_____
_____
_____
_____
_____
_____
_____
_____

PROMPT #30

I am so happy I listened
to my gut when I...

_____

_____

_____

_____

_____

_____

_____

_____

_____

_____

_____

_____

YOUR GIFTS MATTER.
YOUR STORY MATTERS.
YOUR DREAMS MATTER.

-Michael Oher -

Badass Manifesto #7

You Get To Choose

You get to choose how you feel. Your mood. Your reactions. To be happy.

So the next time you feel you don't have control over your life, give yourself some space, breathe, and choose.

Choose to feel good. Choose to be kind to yourself. Choose to celebrate even the small wins.

You always get to choose.

PROMPT #31

Today, I'm going to do one
thing I want, and that is...

_____

_____

_____

_____

_____

_____

_____

_____

_____

_____

_____

_____

_____

_____

_____

PROMPT #32

This one word describes me...

To me it means...

PROMPT #33

Nothing makes me happier than...

_____

_____

_____

_____

_____

_____

_____

_____

_____

_____

_____

_____

_____

PROMPT #34

I've been to lots of places, but
this one inspires me the most...

_____

_____

_____

_____

_____

_____

_____

_____

_____

_____

_____

_____

_____

_____

_____

PROMPT #35

Secretly, I wish...

_____

_____

_____

_____

_____

_____

_____

_____

_____

_____

_____

_____

_____

_____

WE DO NOT NEED MAGIC
TO TRANSFORM OUR WORLD.
WE CARRY ALL OF THE
POWER WE NEED INSIDE
OURSELVES ALREADY.

-J.K. Rowling-

Badass Manifesto #8

You Are Exactly Where You Should Be

Stop comparing yourself to others. You don't really want what they have. If you did, you'd have to take everything in their life. You don't want their life.

You're on your own journey. It might feel like it's going slow, and at times, backwards.

Forget time. Forget goal setting. And just keep telling yourself that you are exactly where you should be.

PROMPT #36

It felt so good to speak
my truth when...

_____

_____

_____

_____

_____

_____

_____

_____

_____

_____

_____

_____

_____

_____

_____

PROMPT #37

My favorite curse word...

It's a favorite because...

PROMPT #38

If I was starring in my own
movie I would be...

_____

_____

_____

_____

_____

_____

_____

_____

_____

_____

_____

_____

_____

_____

_____

_____

PROMPT #39

It's ok that not everyone
"gets me." I'm unique by being...

_____

_____

_____

_____

_____

_____

_____

_____

_____

_____

_____

_____

_____

PROMPT #40

If there were no limits,
I would...

_____
_____
_____
_____
_____
_____
_____
_____
_____
_____
_____
_____
_____

**WHY FIT IN
WHEN YOU WERE BORN
TO STAND OUT?**

-Dr. Seuss-

Badass Manifesto #9

Listen to Your Inner Voice
Not Your Inner Critic

You have a built in guidance system. It's called your gut. And it knows what's up. Always.

So whenever your inner critic rears its ugly head trying to push you down, or make you feel powerless, learn how to listen to your inner voice.

It will always guide you to the right path. It will take you from one simple idea to another, like building blocks, and before you know it, you will have built a skyscraper of amazing ideas.

PROMPT #41

I'm on a billboard. It says...

_____

_____

_____

_____

_____

_____

_____

_____

_____

_____

_____

_____

_____

PROMPT #42

It was so freeing and fun
to take a chance and...

PROMPT #43

I promise myself that I will...

_____

_____

_____

_____

_____

_____

_____

_____

_____

_____

_____

_____

_____

PROMPT #44

I promise myself that I
will not...

_____

_____

_____

_____

_____

_____

_____

_____

_____

_____

_____

_____

_____

_____

_____

PROMPT #45

This person is my inspiration.

Because...

IN ORDER TO
KICK ASS
YOU MUST FIRST
LIFT UP YOUR FOOT.

-Jen Sincero-

Badass Manifesto #10

Enough

You are enough. Just as you are. Without having to do anything, or prove anything, or be anything. You are already enough. Because you exist. You breathe. You are here.

That is reason enough. Believe in your you-ness. Love yourself now. Not when you get to wherever you think you need to be. Now.

Now, you are enough.

PROMPT #46

Something I learned
about myself is...

_____

_____

_____

_____

_____

_____

_____

_____

_____

_____

_____

_____

_____

_____

PROMPT #47

This song always puts
me in a good mood...

When I hear it, I start...

PROMPT #48

I want to honor my story
because it's my own (even the
hard stuff). So every day I will...

_____

_____

_____

_____

_____

_____

_____

_____

_____

_____

_____

_____

_____

PROMPT #49

Today, this is what I will say
YES to, and what I will say
NO to...

_____

_____

_____

_____

_____

_____

_____

_____

_____

_____

_____

_____

_____

PROMPT #50

I feel joy when...

1.
2.
3.
4.
5.
6.
7.
8.
9.
10.

PROMPT #51

The next time my gremlin rears
its ugly head, this is how I'm
going to show it who's boss...

Dear #!@%&* Gremlin,

You are a big pain, and I need you to ——————
(go away/get lost/stop/annoy someone else)

You come knocking on my door every time I'm about
to do something bold and —————— .
(courageous/scary/fun/adventurous)

You act like you —————— me, but I know
better.   (adore/love/worship/idolize/admire)

So, cut it out. I don't need your —————— .
(advice/suggestions/flattery/protection)

This relationship is —————— !
(kaput/over/done/ancient history)

PROMPT #52

This is how I'm sharing me
with the world...

_____

_____

_____

_____

_____

_____

_____

_____

_____

_____

_____

_____

_____

_____

I WISH YOU COULD SEE
YOURSELF THROUGH MY EYES.
THEN YOU WOULD KNOW JUST
HOW *AMAZING* YOU ARE.

-Katrina Mayer-